L for
Love

and **Rent-a-Poet**

Chris Culshaw

Press

L for Love

1

Meeting Ellen

Smash! Crash! Clatter! I was on the floor of the mini-market, under an avalanche of Coke cans. A hand appeared. A girl's hand. Slim, sun-tanned, and with bright red finger-nails. A voice said, 'You going to lie there all day?' I took hold of the hand. It pulled. A strong pull. 'This girl lifts weights,' I thought. I stood up, knee-deep in Coke cans. The girl looked me up and down. My face was the colour of her nail varnish. 'You need L-plates on that trolley,' she said.

'I'll give you a hand,' I stammered. I bent down and picked up some cans of Coke. 'Where shall I...?'

'Over here.' She took the cans and stacked them at the end of the aisle. 'It took me half an hour to make that tower this morning. Very artistic it was.'

She was wearing a green overall. It had a name on the pocket: Shane. 'You've got an unusual name,' I said. I pointed to her name

tag. She laughed. 'How many girls do you know called Shane? This isn't my overall. I only work here three hours on a Saturday. I don't get my own overall, so I have to borrow Shane's.'

'Lucky Shane,' I said to myself and passed her a few more cans. 'What's your real name?' I asked, suddenly feeling brave.

'Ellen. What's yours?'

'Robin. But everyone calls me Birdie. Not very original, is it?'

She smiled. 'Could be worse. I've got a cousin called Rachel Starr. She's nearly ten and she's really tiny. Guess what she gets called?'

'No idea.'

Ellen started to sing: 'Twinkle, twinkle, little star...' Then she turned to go. 'Got to finish filling the freezer, or the boss will give me some earache.'

As I was waiting at the check-out, I watched her filling up the freezer. She was a bit older than me. Fifteen... sixteen, maybe. She was tall and slim. She was wearing flip-flops and I could see her toes. Her toe-nails were bright red, just like her finger-nails. She had red hair and freckles on her face and arms.

I paid at the check-out. As I was leaving the shop, Ellen called out, 'Don't forget your L-plates next time!'

2
New Image

Thump! Thump! Thump! My sister Laura was banging on the bathroom door. 'You've been in there half an hour,' she moaned. 'I need to go to the loo.'

'Use the downstairs loo,' I muttered.

'I don't like the downstairs loo. There are spiders in there.'

I opened the door. 'About time too,' she said. She sniffed. 'Have you been using my body spray?'

'No,' I lied, and ran downstairs.

When she came downstairs a few minutes later, I could tell she was going to give me a hard time. 'Mum, why does our Robin smell like a perfume shop? And why is he wearing his best jeans and trainers? And why has he washed his hair twice this week?'

I was heading for the door. 'I'm going shopping for Gran,' I said.

Mum laughed. 'Oh yes? And I'm a one-eyed wombat.'

3
Star Performance

Ellen was standing next to the freezer, by a mountain of beef burgers and fish fingers.

'Hello, Shane,' I said, trying my best to be very casual.

She smiled and said, 'Hello, Birdie.' She looked at my trolley. 'Tut. Tut. Still driving without L-plates.'

'What are you doing?' I said, looking over her shoulder.

'Getting frost-bite. Feel.' She put her hand on my arm. It was freezing! 'But you know what they say,' she said. '"Cold hands ... warm heart."'

I put a few things in my trolley and went back towards the freezer. Ellen was stacking some empty boxes. It was now or never. If I didn't ask her now, I never would. 'Do you ever go to the disco at St Luke's?' I said.

She shrugged. 'Yes. Usually on a Friday
night. Sometimes Saturday.'

'You going tonight?'

'Yes.'

'See you there, then?'

'I suppose so. I'll be there about nine.'

And before she could change her mind, I headed off for the check-out at top speed.

I couldn't believe it. I'd asked her out. She'd said 'Yes'! All week I'd been going over and over that scene. I had locked myself in the bathroom for hours. I had looked into the mirror and said: 'Ellen, will you go out with me?' or 'Ellen, are you doing anything tonight?' or 'Fancy going to the disco tonight, Ellen?'

I couldn't believe it. I was brilliant. I deserved an Oscar.

4
Disco Disaster

I got to St Luke's about nine. The first person I saw was Ellen. I strolled over to her, trying to be casual. 'Hello, Shane,' I said, sitting down next to her. I waited for her to say, 'Hello, Birdie,' but she didn't. She seemed a bit on edge. She was looking around – as if she was expecting someone. Then I saw there were two drinks on the table.

Ellen turned to me and said, 'At the shop... I think I gave you the wrong idea. When you

said "Are you going to the disco?"... were you asking me out?'

I nodded. I could see what was coming next. It was in her face. She looked sorry. 'It never... I mean, at the time. I didn't think.' She looked around again. 'I've got a boyfriend. Dave Dickson. Do you know him?'

I shook my head. I was going to say, 'What's he got that I haven't?' when he came walking over. What he had were muscles, a Hollywood sun-tan, and more stubble than a hedgehog. He sat down. I tried to make myself invisible. 'This is Robin,' Ellen said.

He nodded. 'The strong silent type,' I thought. He picked up his drink. I got up and made my way to the door.

To my surprise, Ellen got up and followed me. 'Hang on, Birdie,' she said. 'Don't go.' I looked over to where Dave was sitting. He was talking to a gang of lads.

I said, 'What's the point? You're here with your boyfriend.'

'I'm sorry. It's all my fault. But don't go. Come over here for a minute.' She took hold of my sleeve and pulled me into the corner. I was looking at Dangerous Dave. I could feel

his big hands round my throat. What was Ellen doing, dragging me into a dark corner...?

'I want you to meet someone,' she said.

'Who?' I said nervously. 'Not another boyfriend? Does this one do karate?'

'Don't be daft, Birdie – it's my sister. I want you to meet my sister Vicky.'

So that was it! Ellen had planned this. 'She got me here to meet her ugly sister,' I thought. 'I bet she's got spots and bad breath. I bet she's got two left feet – size twelve feet. I bet she's a walking jumble sale. I bet she's a beanpole or a midget. I bet all she talks about are horses and girl-guide camping holidays. I bet...'

5
Meeting Vicky

We were standing next to a table in a dark corner of the disco. There was a girl, sitting by herself. It was so dark I could hardly see her. Ellen said, 'Vicky, this is Birdie. That guy I told you about. The one who demolished the mini-market.' A quiet voice from the darkness said, 'Hello.'

Ellen whispered in my ear, 'She's very shy. But she's okay.' Then she was gone.

What could I do? I couldn't run away. I wanted to! I wanted to say, 'Sorry, I've got to get an early night – I'm going sky-diving tomorrow,' or 'Must dash, I'm on Breakfast TV tomorrow – got to get my beauty sleep.'

But there was no way out. I was feeling pretty stupid and I would look even more stupid if I left now.

So I sat down next to Vicky. Just then the music started. It was very loud. I was waiting for Vicky to say something. Five minutes later I realized she was doing the same thing. So I leaned across and shouted to her, 'Do you want to dance?'

She shouted back, 'I can't.'

Just as I thought. She's got two left feet.

Then she leaned across – what a wonderful smell! – and said, 'It's my ankle.' She lifted up her right leg and I could see that she had her ankle in plaster.

'How did you do that?'

'Rock climbing, last weekend. I fell about twenty feet.'

'Interesting,' I said to myself, as I pulled my chair a bit closer to her. 'Do you fancy a drink, Vicky?'

6
First Sight

I went to the bar. It took a while to get served. I was making my way back to the corner where Vicky was sitting when the music stopped. The DJ said, 'Let's take a break,' and the lights came on.

Now I could see Vicky clearly. Did she have spots? Was she ugly? Was she a walking jumble sale? No way! She was just like her sister – only without the red nail varnish!

I gave her the drink and sat down. Suddenly I didn't know what to say. It had been easy in the dark. Then she was just a voice. It was like talking to someone on the phone. Now I felt awkward. And she was *so* shy.

When the lights went down it was easier. But I was so keen to say the right thing that the words came out wrong. Vicky was no better. Between us we must have looked like a pair of eleven-year-olds on our very first date.

As the disco was coming to an end, I leaned over and said, 'Can I walk you home?'

'No,' she said. 'But you can push me.'

Her wheelchair was parked in the cloakroom. Her mother had said that if she went to the disco she had to go in a wheelchair. 'And you don't argue with my mother,' Vicky said, as we left the disco.

I was pushing the chair too fast. Showing off. Trying to be casual. Making a noise like a Formula One racing car. Crashing the gears, burning up the tyres. You can guess what happened. I hit a litter bin and tipped Vicky out onto the pavement.

'Oh, I'm sorry,' I said, helping her back into the chair. 'Are you okay?'

She laughed. 'Ellen was right. You do need L-plates.'

'Oh yes,' I said to myself. 'It's L for Love. Or I'm a one-eyed wombat.'

Rent-a-Poet

1
Secret Valentine

Dave was sitting on the steps behind the gym when his friend Omar came running over.

'I've been looking for you everywhere, Dave,' said Omar. 'Have you done that English homework?'

'Sure. I did it last night,' Dave said.

'Great. If you let me copy it, you will save me from a certain death. I'm already in detention tonight with Mrs Sinclair.'

'What's it worth?' asked Dave.

'How about this?' Omar dropped a Mars bar in his friend's lap.

Dave pulled out his English book and tossed it to Omar. A piece of paper fell out and Omar picked it up. 'Is this it?' He started to read what was written on the sheet.

'You are my Valentine.
I want to go out with you.
Can you guess who wrote this?
Your secret love so true.'

Dave jumped up and snatched the piece of paper. Omar laughed and said, 'In love are we? Who is it?'

'Not telling you.'

'Oh go on, Dave. I'm your best mate. I can keep a secret. Go on, tell me.'

'Promise you'll keep it secret?'

'Cross my heart and hope to die. So, who is your secret heart-throb?'

'Helen James.'

Omar laughed. 'Helen James? You're a hopeless case, Dave.' He picked up Dave's English book and rolled it up so it looked like a megaphone. 'Here is an important

announcement for everyone in Year 9. David Lloyd has gone crazy. At any minute, men in white coats will come and take him away... He seriously thinks he stands a chance of going out with...' Dave snatched the book from Omar and put it in his bag.

'Oh come on, Dave,' said his friend. 'You promised. If I don't do that work I really will get a detention.'

Dave gave him the book and sat eating the Mars bar while Omar copied his homework.

2
Ghost Writer

Omar put his arm round his friend's shoulder as they walked into their form room. 'What you need is a ghost writer,' he said.

'What's a ghost writer?'

'Footballers, boxers, and the like – they use them when they write their life stories. Maradona was a great footballer, but he couldn't spell for toffee. So he paid someone to write his life story – a ghost writer.'

'I still don't see what you're getting at, Omar,' said Dave.

'You really want to go out with Helen the Heartbreaker. Right?

'Right.'

'You want to impress her. Right?'

'Right.'

'With a romantic poem. Right?'

'Right.'

'So you need a ghost writer.'

'Not you, Omar!' Dave laughed.

'Of course not.'

'Then who?'

Omar went over to his locker and opened it. A pile of crumpled papers and muddy PE kit fell out on his head.

'What about Lisa Shapiro?' he said at last. 'She always gets an A-star for English.'

Dave looked doubtful. 'Would she do it? Can she keep a secret?'

Omar stuffed the disgusting heap of rubbish back into his locker. 'If you made it worth her while.' He held up a half-eaten Mars bar. 'I hear she's a chocoholic.'

3
Dave's Advert

Dave was on his way home, crossing the park, when he heard someone call out, 'Hang on, David.' He turned round and saw Lisa Shapiro a few yards behind him.

'Omar said you wanted to see me,' she said.

Dave started to walk on. He was a bit embarrassed. He didn't like to think that Lisa knew about him fancying Helen James. Lisa was in his form. She was okay. She was a bit weird. Green hair, five studs in each ear and two in her nose. But she wasn't catty like some of the other girls.

She caught him up and walked along beside him. 'You on a sponsored silence, Dave? Omar says you're in love. Says you need a ghost writer. Well, here I am: Rent-a-Poet.'

Dave looked at Lisa. 'This has got to be a secret. Promise?'

Lisa put her hand on her heart and said, 'Promise.'

They sat down on a park bench and Lisa got out a pencil and notebook. 'I need some background info. Tell me all about yourself...'

Dave looked a bit uneasy. 'Why?'

'Because you want The Heartbreaker to read my... er, sorry, your poem and think, "Wow. I wonder who wrote this? I'd like to meet this guy." You've got to sell yourself, Dave. Think of the poem as an advert. So just imagine that I'm Helen James and tell me all about your good points...'

Half an hour later they were still sitting on the bench when Omar came past on his way home from school detention. He looked at Dave and grinned, but didn't say anything.

4
Lisa's Poem

The next day Lisa came up to Dave in the form room and slipped him a sheet of neatly folded paper. Dave tucked it in his bag and went off to his first lesson. He didn't get a chance to read the poem until break-time. When he did read it he got a surprise.

At lunch-time Omar found Dave sitting on the gym steps as usual. 'Did it work?'

Dave was beaming from ear to ear. 'Like magic.'

'So you've got a date with Helen the Heartbreaker?'

'No – I'm going out with Rent-a-Poet.'

'With Lisa? How come?'

Dave took the sheet of paper out of his bag. 'This is how come,' he said. 'Read this.' He unfolded it and handed it to Omar.

Dave, you're such a nice guy, a good laugh too.

Going out with Helen James will only make you blue.

Last night as we talked in the park,

and we walked home, later, in the dark,

I got to thinking, about you and me.

We're made for each other. Can't you see?

Don't let The Heartbreaker turn your head

Go out with me - Rent-a-Poet - instead .

D + Me
2 gether
4 ever
Never 2 part

❖ ❖ ❖

OXFORD

UNIVERSITY PRESS

Great Clarendon Street, Oxford OX2 6DP

Oxford New York
Athens Auckland Bangkok Bogotá Buenos Aires Calcutta
Cape Town   Chennai Dar es Salaam Delhi Florence
Hong Kong Istanbul Karachi Kuala Lumpur Madrid
Melbourne Mexico City Mumbai Nairobi Paris
São Paulo Singapore Taipei Tokyo Toronto Warsaw

with associated companies in Berlin Ibadan

Oxford is a trade mark of Oxford University Press

© Chris Culshaw 1996
First published 1996
Reprinted 1999

ISBN 0 19 833578 4

Printed in Great Britain

Illustrations by Gary Wing